Don't come here to sleep or to slumber

For my wonderful Dad and my beloved Beth.

First published 2020 by Mabecron Books Ltd,
Briston Orchard, St Mellion, Saltash, Cornwall, PL12 6RQ.
Illustrated by Sarah Hewitt.
Typeset in Baskerville. Printed in Malaysia

ISBN 978 0 9955028 9 5

The Sleeping Garden

The Sleeping Garden

Written and illustrated by Sarah Hewitt

Mabecron Books

*T*here was once a very special Cornish garden….

The garden was called 'Heligan' and was owned by the wealthy Tremayne family
who gathered rare and exotic plants from every corner of the world.
Over a very long time, Heligan grew more and more beautiful; there was always something magical to see.

It was so glorious that many animals made the garden their home and the air was filled with birdsong.

*I*n time, following in his ancestors' footsteps,
young Jack Tremayne became Squire of Heligan.
Jack took many pictures of his much-loved garden. He liked to travel
and his journeys gave him lots of ideas. With hard work, his visions
were brought to life by the Heligan gardeners.

The Suntrap Garden, inspired by hot, balmy days spent in Italy, had a gentle,
calming fountain and a spreading kiwi vine for shade.

His most fantastic creation was the spectacular Jungle, resplendent with giant tree
ferns, bamboo and many other exotic and tropical plants.

*H*eligan was also a very practical garden.

The 'Productive Gardens' as they were called, contained many varieties of fruit and vegetables. Melons, peaches and grapes were nurtured in huge, heated greenhouses.

The gardeners quickly learned how to look after these exotic plants and were able to produce large quantities of delicious fruit. This valuable knowledge was passed down to each new generation.

*D*elicate pineapples were grown in special pits covered by protective glass frames. They were heated with fresh horse manure which reached such high temperatures that there was even a risk of fire.

This meant that the youngest gardener at Heligan had to be on call throughout the night, to check on the rare and precious fruit.

Through the hard work of Jack and the gardeners, the garden continued to flourish.

But this peace was about to come to an end. In August 1914 war was declared.

Some of the young gardeners of Heligan enlisted to fight for their country. Shortly before they left for war, they wrote their names on a wall in the room they called the Thunderbox Room.
The young men did not want to be forgotten.

Above their names was the motto, 'Don't come here to sleep or to slumber.'

But that was exactly what was about to happen to Heligan….

*T*he Great War lasted four long years.

It had been a harsh and bloody fight. Of the thirteen brave Heligan men who went to war, only four returned.

The Great House became a hospital for injured officers, and no one had the time to work in the garden.
Some of the trees were felled for the war effort but the rest of the garden was neglected.

Jack had been too old to fight in the war and he had been very lonely without his friends, the gardeners.
He missed them dearly and eventually he left Heligan, never to return.

'I can no longer live with the ghosts' he murmured as he locked the gates for the last time.

As the years passed, the gardens were lost.

Creepers enveloped the glasshouses. Weeds engulfed the Suntrap Garden.
The Jungle grew dark and impenetrable.

Heligan, no longer a welcoming place for birds and
animals, was silent and forgotten.
The garden, as if grieving, fell into a deep
and lonely sleep.

*M*any silent years passed until one harsh winter a devastating storm raged across Cornwall.

The wind and rain beat down, attacking the landscape, uprooting ancient trees and destroying everything in its path.

It seemed as if this would be the end for Heligan and what remained of its sleeping grandeur.

'I can no longer live with the ghosts'

*B*ut the Great Storm had stirred the Sleeping Garden.

Local people began to remember the stories of Heligan
and two of them were invited to explore
the remnants of Squire Jack's garden.

Through an open door,
they took their first steps into
a magical lost world.

The men were called Tim and John.
Together they fought their way through creepers and vines,
starting to uncover all that had been hidden.

Giant rhododendrons towered above and huge, derelict glasshouses
appeared in front of them. They were drawn deeper into Heligan's
mystery but still, the gardens remained silent….

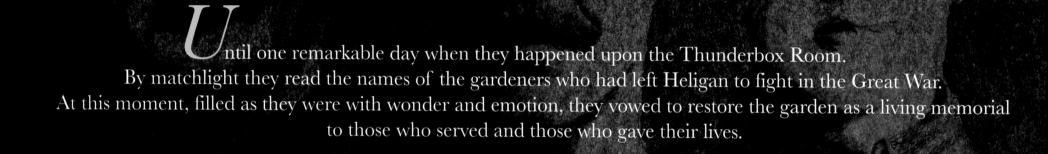

*U*ntil one remarkable day when they happened upon the Thunderbox Room.
By matchlight they read the names of the gardeners who had left Heligan to fight in the Great War.
At this moment, filled as they were with wonder and emotion, they vowed to restore the garden as a living memorial
to those who served and those who gave their lives.

Charles Ball, d.1918
John George Barron, d.1916
Percy Carhart, d.1917
Charles Dyer, d.1918
William Robins Guy, d.1918
William Samuel Hunkin, d.1914

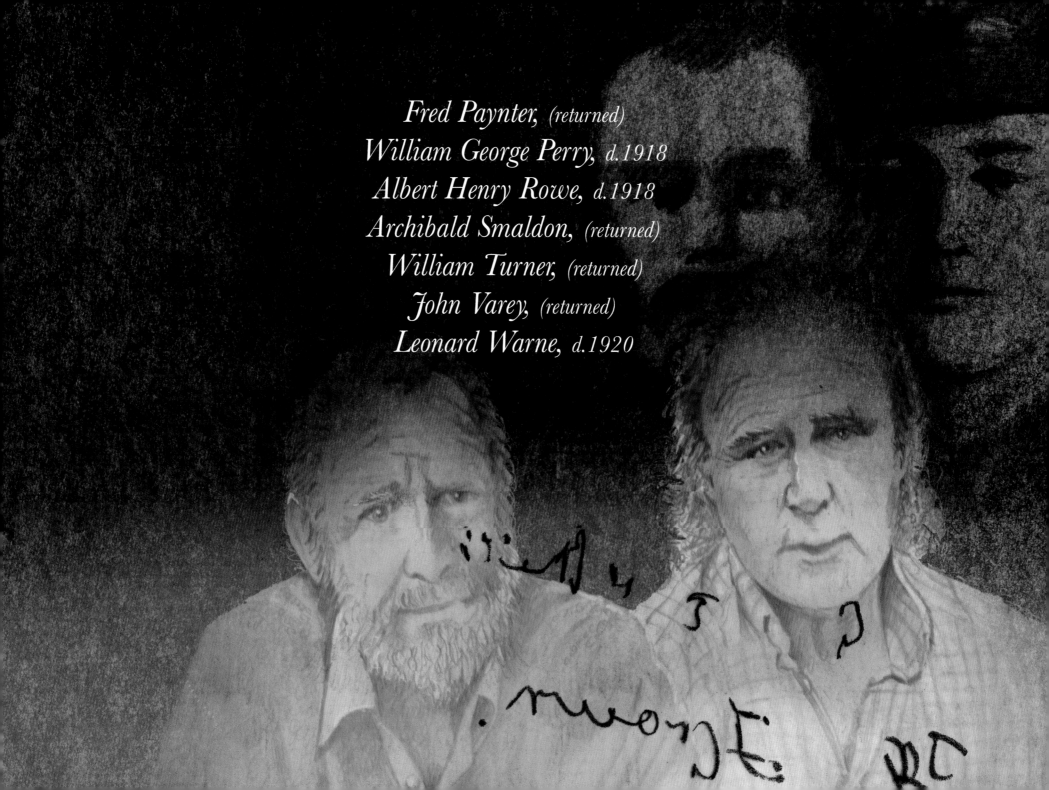

Fred Paynter, *(returned)*
William George Perry, *d.1918*
Albert Henry Rowe, *d.1918*
Archibald Smaldon, *(returned)*
William Turner, *(returned)*
John Varey, *(returned)*
Leonard Warne, *d.1920*

*V*olunteers were signed up. Guided by the legacy of the gardeners'
workbooks and Squire Jack's photographs, they embarked on the huge task ahead.
They cleared the weeds, the brambles and the creepers.
They repaired the greenhouses.
They undertook new planting using traditional tools and methods.

*H*eligan is again a sanctuary for wildlife, and people flock to see the reawakened garden.
Now visitors can stroll amongst the giant rhododendrons and gaze up through the stunning canopies of colour.
They can also experience Jack's Jungle and the Suntrap Garden, both as magnificent as they were all those years ago.

*E*ven the storm-damaged trees have been transformed into
magical sculptures for all to enjoy.

The Mud Maid sleeps peacefully in the woodland
as the Giant keeps a cheeky eye on everyone who visits!

Yet the garden still holds some secrets, for it is said that Heligan is haunted….

*T*here was a day when visitors to the Melon Yard watched in stunned awe; one by one the lids on the forcing pots were mysteriously lifted, followed by a loud sigh.

Many wondered who the invisible spirit might be?

'I can finally live with the ghosts.'

In memory of the Heligan gardeners.
Remembering those who died and those who returned from the First World War.

Thank you to my lovely Richard for his support and eternal optimism.

With thanks to Karen Barry, Peter and Maggie Lavis, Candy Smit and Lorna Tremayne
for their valuable contributions and encouragement, and Pam Smy for teaching me how to draw.

*D*on't come here to sleep or to slumber
Reminds many of the few,
Who planted little acorns so mighty oak trees grew.
Felled to help the kingdom fight the War that claimed their lives,
The men left more than empty hearts, sad orphans, widowed wives.
Bereft, the creeping vines enveloped once neatly tended grounds,
And within the Sleeping Garden, silence was its sound.